¡Chévere!

Spanish for Caribbean Secondary Schools

Activity Book 1

Anne-María Bankay

Ingrid Kemchand

Paulette Ramsay

Elaine Watson-Grant

PEARSON

Longman

Pearson Education Limited
Edinburgh Gate
Harlow
Essex CM20 2EJ
England
and Associated Companies throughout the World

www.longmancaribbean.com

Carlong Publishers (Caribbean) Limited
33 Second Street
Newport West
Kingston 13
Jamaica

Lexicon Trinidad Limited
LP# 48 Boundary Road
San Juan
Trinidad

Third impression 2008
ISBN 978-0-582-85319-5

Prepared for publication by Cathy May
Illustrated by Juliet Breese and Peter Wilkes (Simon Girling Associates).

Printed in China
EPC/03

Contents

¡Hola, mis amigos!

In each chapter of this Activity book, you will find interesting activities to help you practise what you learn as you go through each chapter of your Students' Book 1. There are many puzzles, fill-in-the-blanks, matching exercises and other fun activities that will encourage you to use your creativity and thinking skills. There are also additional activities linked to the ¡Chévere! CD. For these activities you will see a CD icon with the title of the activity. Your teacher will play the CD track for you. Listen carefully in order to do these activities well.

And now, let's have some fun! It's time to apply all that you have learnt!

1 ¡Hola!

A ¡Bienvenidos al mundo hispano!

Look at the map below. Label in Spanish the names of all the countries where Spanish is the official language.

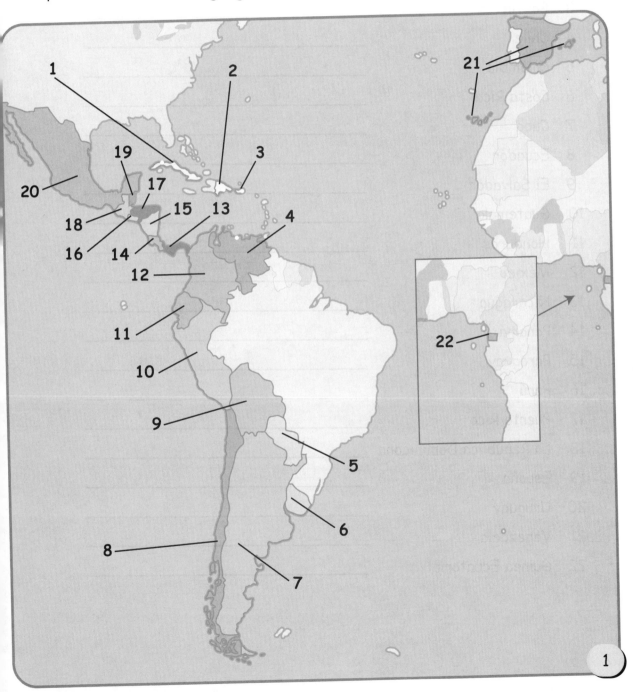

B ¿Cuál es la capital?

Write in Spanish the capital of each Spanish-speaking country listed.

1 Argentina _____

2 Belice _____

3 Bolivia _____

4 Chile _____

5 Colombia _____

6 Costa Rica _____

7 Cuba _____

8 Ecuador _____

9 El Salvador _____

10 Guatemala _____

11 Honduras _____

12 México _____

13 Nicaragua _____

14 Panamá _____

15 Paraguay _____

16 Perú

17 Puerto Rico _____

18 La República Dominicana _____

19 España _____

20 Uruguay _____

21 Venezuela _____

22 Guinea Ecuatorial _____

C Situaciones

Write suitable responses in Spanish to the following situations.

1   It is the first day of school and there are two Spanish speakers in your class. How do you greet one of them?

_____

2   How do you introduce yourself?

_____

3   How do you ask his or her name?

_____

4   How do you introduce an old friend to your new friend?

_____

5   What does your friend say to express pleasure at meeting the new student?

_____

6   What do you say as you return to your seat?

_____

7   What does your teacher say to welcome the entire class?

_____

8   What does your teacher say to welcome a Spanish-speaking girl?

_____

D ¡A contar!

Count in Spanish and add the number of images in each row.

Write the total in Spanish in the spaces provided.

1   ☎ ☎ ☎ ☎   _____

2   🍎🍎🍎🍎🍎🍎   _____

3   ♣ ♣ ♣   _____

4   ❄ ❄ ❄ ❄ ❄ ❄   _____

5   ✡ ✡ ✡ ✡ ✡ ✡ ✡ ✡   _____

6   ●●●●●●●●●●●●   _____

7   ▼   _____

8   ❋ ❋ ❋ ❋ ❋ ❋ ❋ ❋   _____

9   ☞ ☞ ☞ ☞ ☞ ☞ ☞ ☞ ☞   _____

10   → → → → →   _____

11   ◆◆◆◆◆◆◆◆◆◆◆◆◆   _____

12   ✝✝✝✝✝✝✝✝✝✝✝✝✝✝   _____

13   ☞ ☞ ☞ ☞ ☞ ☞ ☞ ☞ ☞ ☞ ☞ ☞   _____

14   ✳ ✳ ✳ ✳ ✳ ✳ ✳ ✳ ✳ ✳   _____

15   ✈ ✈   _____

E Sopa de letras – mi clase de español

Find at least 20 Spanish words that you learned in the first three lessons of your Students' Book. Write the Spanish and English equivalent for each word you find.

B	A	T	I	R	O	Ñ	E	S	E	S	Í	A	P
E	I	B	Ñ	É	G	R	A	C	I	A	S	L	O
R	S	E	S	P	A	Ñ	O	L	Q	U	I	F	V
E	J	E	N	C	A	N	T	A	D	O	E	A	O
V	X	A	R	V	O	C	Í	A	H	L	T	B	C
É	V	T	U	O	E	O	Z	Y	O	B	N	E	A
H	M	Y	Í	T	A	N	E	J	L	K	E	T	B
C	A	R	I	B	E	R	I	Ñ	A	P	M	O	U
A	M	N	Z	R	B	O	U	D	G	H	L	Í	L
T	I	Q	U	M	S	P	I	L	O	H	A	Z	A
A	G	Y	O	M	P	O	E	T	A	S	U	Q	R
R	A	N	D	I	S	Ñ	O	C	Y	U	G	L	I
E	L	R	A	L	U	G	E	R	E	S	I	L	O
A	C	H	I	S	P	A	N	O	E	C	H	É	V

1 _____   11 _____

2 _____   12 _____

3 _____   13 _____

4 _____   14 _____

5 _____   15 _____

6 _____   16 _____

7 _____   17 _____

8 _____   18 _____

9 _____   19 _____

10 _____   20 _____

2 Amigos nuevos

A Crucigrama – amigos nuevos

Use the clues to complete the puzzle in Spanish.

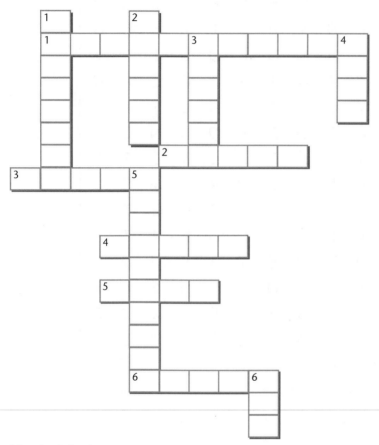

Vertical (↓)

1 Mi _____ es García Pérez.

2 _____ a la escuela secundaria de Montevideo.

3 ¿Cuál es tu primer _____?

4 ¿De dónde _____?

5 Soy un _____ nuevo.

6 _____ de Panamá.

Horizontal (→)

1 Déjame _____.

2 _____ doce años.

3 ¿_____ vives?

4 Hasta _____, mi amigo.

5 _____ en Puerto Rico.

6 ¿Cómo _____?

B Situaciones

Write suitable responses in Spanish for the following situations.

1   You want to know where your teacher is from. What do you ask?

    _____

2   What does he/she reply?

    _____

3   How do you ask a friend his/her age?

    _____

4   Your classmates want to know where you are from. What do you tell
    them?

    _____

5   You and a friend are chatting during break. The bell goes and she has
    to go to class. What does she say?

    _____

6   How do you ask someone which school he/she attends?

    _____

7   How do you ask a friend for his/her address?

    _____

8   How do you give your address?

    _____

C Déjame presentarme...

Write the questions that were asked to get these answers.

1   Me llamo Elena.

    _____

2   Vivo en Lares.

    _____

3   Soy de Venezuela.

    _____

4   Tengo trece años.

    _____

5   Asisto a la escuela secundaria de San José.

    _____

6   Sí, soy una estudiante nueva.

    _____

7   Bien, gracias.

    _____

8   Sí, vivo con mi familia.

    _____

9   Vivo en la Avenida Prima Vista, número 13.

    _____

10   Mi correo electrónico es bori@pr.com

    _____

D ¿Quién soy yo?

Look at Juan's ID card. Pretend you are Juan. Write a paragraph about yourself based on the information given on the ID card.

Nombre:	Juan
Apellido:	Batista
Edad:	12 años
Nacionalidad:	cubano
País de domicilio:	Estados Unidos
Dirección:	Calle Santo Domingo, número 2
Escuela:	Escuela secundaria de San Mateo

_____

_____

_____

_____

_____

_____

_____

_____

_____

_____

3 ¡Ésta es mi familia!

This is Carlos' family.
Write on each line what
he would say as he
introduces each person.

2. The mother – Señora Romero

1. The father –
Señor Romero

4. The 5-
year-old
brother
– Pedrito

3. The 18-
year-old
sister –
Marcela

1 _____

2 _____

3 _____

4 _____

B Situaciones

Write suitable responses in Spanish for the following situations.

1   How do you ask a female friend how many persons there are in her family?

_____

2   Your friend's family is very large. What does she reply?

_____

3   What do you exclaim?

_____

4   Your friend shows you a picture of her older sister. What does she say as she shows you the picture?

_____

5   How do you tell your friend that her sister is very pretty?

_____

6   How do you ask your friend if she has any brothers?

_____

7   Your friend has two brothers. What does she reply?

_____

8   How does your friend tell you what their names are?

_____

C Mi familia

Look at the list of words. Find the Spanish equivalent for each word in the puzzle and then write the word in the space provided.

```
P  A  D  R  E  Ñ  C  G  H  E  R  D  A  M
A  J  E  U  S  I  K  E  D  S  I  A  Y  F
V  I  S  Q  P  U  V  A  E  A  L  M  K  I
Y  H  Í  Y  O  H  X  T  T  Í  O  Ñ  U  X
L  A  G  F  S  J  N  Z  J  N  L  I  S  I
U  D  Z  E  A  E  Y  G  A  T  E  V  O  S
S  O  Q  U  I  L  P  M  S  O  U  C  L  O
A  L  M  R  M  H  R  I  D  G  B  H  E  M
Ñ  F  A  B  U  E  L  A  R  I  A  D  U  I
C  P  X  E  H  F  Ñ  Y  C  V  P  Í  B  R
M  O  Ñ  U  X  U  O  G  S  E  R  D  A  P
Y  T  Q  J  C  A  T  Z  K  U  J  W  S  Y
E  S  P  O  S  O  Í  C  V  I  Q  M  I  U
Z  L  F  Y  A  N  A  M  R  E  H  C  B  Ñ
```

1   mother   _____

2   father   _____

3   brother   _____

4   sister   _____

5   grandfather   _____

6   grandmother   _____

7   godson   _____

8   uncle   _____

9   aunt   _____

10   brother-in-law

     _____   _____

11   great grandparents

     _____

12   parents   _____

13   husband   _____

14   wife   _____

15   cousins   _____

16   relatives   _____

D El árbol familiar de Elvira I

Look at Elvira's family tree. Complete the statements based on the family tree.

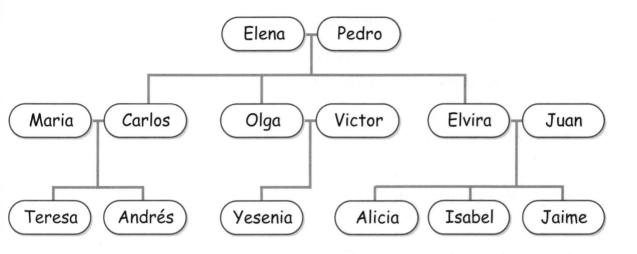

1   Elena y Pedro son los _____ de Teresa.

2   Yesenia y Jaime son _____.

3   Elvira es la _____ de Olga y Carlos.

4   Carlos es el _____ de Teresa y Andrés.

5   María es la _____ de Jaime.

6   Juan es el _____ de Elvira.

7   Víctor es el _____ de María y Elvira.

8   Teresa y Andrés son los _____ de Olga.

9   Jaime es el _____ de Isabel.

10 Olga y Víctor son los _____ de Yesenia.

Look once more at Elvira's family tree. Answer the questions in Spanish, using full sentences.

1   ¿Cuántas personas hay en la familia de Elvira?

   _____

2   ¿Cuántas hermanas tiene Jaime?

   _____

3   ¿Cómo se llaman?

   _____

4   ¿Quién es el padre de Isabel?

   _____

5   ¿Cuántos hermanos tienen Olga y Elvira?

   _____

6   ¿Cómo se llaman las primas de Teresa?

   _____

7   ¿Quién es el padre de Olga?

   _____

8   ¿Cuántos tíos tiene Teresa?

   _____

9   ¿Es María la esposa de Víctor?

   _____

10   ¿Es una familia grande o pequeña?

   _____

4 ¡Celebremos!

Complete the dialogue with the words provided.

| tiene | fiesta | hasta | catorce | cuántos | luego |

Javier: Hola, Mercedes. ¿Sabes? La (1)_____de Conchita es mañana.

Mercedes: Sí, recuerdo. Es su cumpleaños.

Javier: Conchita (2)_____ doce años. ¿(3)_____ años tienes tú, Mercedes?

Mercedes: Pues, tengo trece.

Javier: Yo tengo (4)_____. Hasta (5)_____, Mercedes.

Mercedes: Adiós, Javier, (6)_____ mañana.

B Crucigrama

Complete this crossword. All the clues are about the days of the week.

Across

2　One seventh of a week.

3　Seven days altogether.

5　Longest day of the Spanish week.

6　First day of the week in Mexico.

Down

1　No school today... Watching cartoons perhaps?

4　Thank God it's ...

C Los números

Work out the answers to each of the problems below. Fill the answers in the blank spaces provided.

Ejemplo: Dieciocho y tres son ___veintiuno___ .

1　Treinta y uno menos diecinueve son _____ .

2　Veintidós y siete son _____ .

3　_____ y catorce son veintinueve .

4　Quince menos cuatro son _____ .

5　Trece y _____ son veintitrés .

D ¿Cuándo es el cumpleaños?

Listen to the short dialogue on track 14 and fill in the grid with the correct information about their birthdays.

	Javier	Mercedes	Araceli
Fecha	2		
Mes		noviembre	

E Sopaletras

Find the months of the year – los meses del año.

o	r	c	n	p	v	i	d	j	e	h
s	f	t	a	g	d	o	i	l	u	j
f	e	d	r	v	y	a	c	s	f	m
n	b	p	c	a	g	o	i	s	q	a
c	r	s	m	o	c	c	e	j	r	t
d	e	m	s	e	g	t	m	k	c	l
u	r	t	d	l	i	u	b	n	m	i
n	o	v	i	e	m	b	r	e	s	y
c	m	p	m	o	o	r	e	n	e	s
d	a	b	r	i	l	e	x	r	s	l
f	r	g	t	n	a	z	v	b	r	e
e	z	v	f	u	o	y	p	g	o	t
h	o	n	c	j	r	k	u	t	l	j

F Una carta de Lorenzo

Read the following letter which Lorenzo writes to Nicolás, then answer the questions that follow in English.

San Juan, 15 de diciembre de 2005

Querido Nicolás,

¿Qué tal? ¿Cómo está tu familia? Tengo una noticia interesante.

Hay una fiesta de Quinceaños mañana para mi amiga Carla. La fiesta es muy grande porque hay muchos invitados.

La celebración tiene lugar en un hotel fabuloso que se llama Vista del Mar, que está en la Avenida Alicante, número 21.

Tengo un traje muy elegante.

Escríbeme pronto.

Tu amigo,

Lorenzo

1 What is taking place tomorrow?

_____

2 What does Lorenzo say about the party?

_____

3 Why is he of this opinion?

_____

4 Where will the event take place?

_____

5 What will Lorenzo be wearing?

_____

6 What does Lorenzo want Nicolás to do quickly?

_____

G Una invitación

Read the letter again and complete the invitation below with the correct information.

El Señor Castillo

y

La Señora Guillermo de Castillo

invitan

al Señor (1) _____ Pacheco

a la celebración de

la (2) _____ de (3) _____

de su (4) _____ Carla Margarita

Fecha: (5) _____

Hora: 7 de la tarde

Dirección: Hotel (6) _____

Avenida Alicante, (7) _____

Traje: (8) _____

Se ruega respuesta.

H ¿Qué fecha es?

Write out the dates indicated below.

APRIL 1st

APRIL 30

June

M	T	W	Th	F	S	S
	1	2	3	4	5	6
7	8	9	⑩	11	12	13
14	15	16	17	18	19	20
21	22	23	24	25	26	㉗
28	29	30				

OCTOBER

M 1	W 17
T 2	Th 18
W 3	F 19
Th 4	S 20
F 5	S 21
S 6	M 22
S 7	T 23
M 8	W 24
T 9	Th 25
W 10	F 26
Th 11	S 27
F ⑫	S 28
S 13	M 29
S 14	T 30
M 15	W ㉛
T 16	

December

MON	4	11	18	㉕
TUE	5	12	19	㉖
WED	6	13	20	27
THU	7	14	21	28
FRI	1	8	15	22	29
SAT	2	9	16	23	30
SUN	3	10	17	24	31

1 _____

2 _____

3 _____

4 _____

5 _____

6 _____

7 _____

8 _____

I Correo por Internet

Complete this e-mail message that Alicia sends to a new pen-pal by filling in the blank spaces with the appropriate words.

Me (1)_____ Alicia y (2)_____ catorce años.

Mi (3)_____ es el 4 de marzo y siempre hay una fiesta en

mi casa. Asisto a una (4)_____ secundaria que se llama Santa

Teresa. Tengo (5)_____ de inglés y matemáticas todos los

(6)_____. Los profesores son excelentes en mi escuela.

Tengo muchos (7)_____ pero mi mejor amigo es Oswaldo.

Es inteligente y simpático.

Hasta pronto, Un abrazo de tu (8)_____,

Alicia

J Fechas importantes

Fill in the Spanish names for the celebrations held on the dates below. Discuss with your teacher how they are celebrated in Spanish-speaking countries.

1   el veinticinco de diciembre _____

2   el primero de enero _____

3   el veinticuatro de diciembre _____

4   el treinta y uno de diciembre _____

5   el seis de enero _____

6   el dos de noviembre _____

K Las celebraciones

Find out more about one holiday that is not celebrated in your country. Do a brief report on it. Include a photograph or a drawing.

Fecha:

Nombre de la celebración:

Ilustración o foto:

_____

_____

_____

_____

_____

_____

5 Lo nuestro

A ¿Qué hay en la mesa?

Write the names of the items shown on the table in Spanish, in the spaces below. To practise your numbers, you can say how many of each item you see.

1 _____

2 _____

3 _____

4 _____

5 _____

6 _____.

B Preguntas y respuestas

Match the answers on the left to the questions in the column on the right.

1	Muy bien.	a	¿Cómo se llama tu hermano?
2	Tengo trece.	b	¿Me permite tocar la guitarra, Javier?
3	Se llama Enrique.	c	¿Usan el peso en Guatemala?
4	Hay cinco.	d	¿Nueve por cinco, Ana?
5	¡Cómo no!	e	¿Es tu regla, Andrew?
6	No, el quetzal.	f	¿Cuántos años tienes?
7	Son cuarenta y cinco.	g	¿Es un libro, Araceli?
8	Lápices y goma.	h	¿Cuántas personas hay en tu familia?
9	Sí, profe.	i	¿Qué tienes en la mano?
10	No, es un cuaderno.	j	¿Qué tal, amigo?

C ¿Masculino o feminino? ¿Singular o plural?

Place the words below in the correct column, depending on their number and gender. Look back to your vocabulary lists to make sure you have chosen the right column.

lápices   mochila   relojes   ventana   abanico   carreta   días
exposición   muñecas   pupitre   pared   embajador   literatura
computadoras   regalo   bolígrafo

El	La	Los	Las

D Hay muchos

Ana is helping her teacher check a list of school supplies that have just been received. They have more than one of each item. Complete the sentences making the items plural.

¿Hay un cuaderno, Ana?

Sí, profesora, hay unos cuadernos.

1   **Profesora:**   ¿Hay una calculadora, Ana?

    Ana: Sí, profesora, hay _____.

2   **Profesora:**   ¿Hay un libro, Ana?

    Ana: Sí, profesora, hay _____.

3   **Profesora:**   ¿Hay un lápiz, Ana?

    Ana: Sí, profesora, hay _____.

4   **Profesora:**   ¿Hay un rotulador, Ana?

    Ana: Sí, profesora, hay _____.

5   **Profesora:**   ¿Hay un mapa, Ana?

    Ana: Sí, profesora, hay _____.

6   **Profesora:**   ¿Hay un sacapuntas, Ana?

    Ana: Sí, profesora, hay _____.

7   **Profesora:**   ¿Hay un disco compacto, Ana?

    Ana: Sí, profesora, hay _____.

8   **Profesora:**   ¿Hay un disquete, Ana?

    Ana: Sí, profesora, hay _____.

9   **Profesora:**   ¿Hay un reloj, Ana?

    Ana: Sí, profesora, hay _____.

10 **Profesora:**   ¿Hay una goma, Ana?

    Ana: Sí, profesora, hay _____.

E Revuelto de palabras

Look carefully at the following groups of words and rearrange each group to make a sentence. Be sure to use the correct punctuation.

1   puertas, y, una, hay, la, en, clase, ventana, dos.

_____

2   en, tengo, muchas, mi, cosas, mochila.

_____

3   unos, mesa, hay, en, cuadernos, la.

_____

4   la, por, asignaturas, tarde, tienes, cuales.

_____

5   abanico, la, preciosa, y, es, carreta, muy, el, bonito es.

_____

F Los negativos

Give a negative response (using **no**) to these questions.

1   ¿Es Mercedes de Puerto Rico?

_____

2   ¿Tienes aritmética hoy?

_____

3   ¿Hay libros en el pupitre, Javier?

_____

4   ¿Tienes hermanos, Pepe?

_____

5   ¿Están en la clase los estudiantes?

_____

6 ¿Hay muchos lápices en la mochila?

_____

7 ¿Es esto un telegrama?

_____

8 ¿Necesitas mi goma, amigo?

_____

9 ¿Hoy es el cumpleaños de Andrew?

_____

10 ¿Tienes algo en la mano, Celi?

_____

G Un correo electrónico

Listen to track 21 on the CD and fill in the missing words. The number of blanks indicates the number of missing letters.

Hoy (1) _ _ el Día de la Cultura en la (2) _ _ _ _ _ _ _.

Hay (3) _ _ _ _ _ _ estudiantes y profesores y muchas (4) _ _ _ _ _

de interés. En la exposición, hay cosas muy (5) _ _ _ _ _ _ de países

(6) _ _ _ _ _ _ _ _, por ejemplo una (7) _ _ _ _ _ _ _ y un abanico.

También, hay una (8) _ _ _ _ _ _ _ _ _ y un sombrero. Hay (9) _ _ _ _ _ _

de Venezuela y tortillas de México. El (10) _ _ _ _ _ _ _ _ _ de Costa

Rica visita la escuela y habla con algunos estudiantes.

H Completa las conversaciones

mi   mis   tu   tus   su   sus

*Hint: Figure out if each conversation is familiar (**tu/tus**) or polite (**su/sus**).*

Araceli: ¿Tienes (1) _____ bolígrafo, Andrew? (**my**)

Andrew: Si, Celi, tengo (2) _____ boli y también (3)_____ lápices.
(**your**)

Michael: ¿Cómo se llama tu amigo de correspondencia, Mercedes?

Mercedes: (4)_____ nombre es Lorenzo. (**his**)

Michael: ¿Y donde vive?

Mercedes: Vive en Colombia, pero (5)_____ padres viven en Estados
Unidos. (**his**)

Profesor: ¿Quién tiene mi regla, alumnos?

Alumnos: (6)_____ regla está en la mesa, profesora. (**your**)

Profesor: ¿Y (7)_____ tareas, alumnos? (**your**)

Alumnos: Están en casa, profesor.

Mercedes: Buenas tardes, señora Ramdial, ¿Están en casa (8)_____
hijos? (**your**)

Sra. Ramdial: No, Mercedes. (9)_____ amigos no están en casa.
(**your**)

Javier: Señor, hay algo de (10)_____ país en la exposición? (**your**)

Embajador: Sí, joven, y de otros países también.

Javier: ¿Cuándo es el cumpleaños de Mercedes?

Ana: (11)_____ cumpleaños es mañana. (**her**)

Araceli: ¿Dónde están Michael y Ana?

Andrew: Están con (12)_____ papá. (**their**)

I Mi horario

Fill in the subjects you study at school in the timetable below. After your teacher has corrected it, you can make a copy to keep for reference.

Nombre: _____   Apellido: _____

Clase: _____   Escuela: _____

Lunes	Martes	Miércoles	Jueves	Viernes

RECREO

ALMUERZO

6 ¡A charlar!

A La vida familiar

Listen to the dialogue on track 23 of the CD. Read the questions below and make some short notes as you listen. Then write the answers to the questions in Spanish.

1 ¿Cómo se llama el programa?

_____

2 ¿Cómo es la familia de Mercedes?

_____

3 ¿Por qué vive Mercedes con su mamá?

_____

4 ¿Cuántas personas hay en la familia de Ana?

_____

5 ¿Con quién vive Javier?

_____

6 ¿Dónde viven los padres de Javier?

_____

Use the information in the following passage to fill out a data sheet about Adriana for a club she is joining.

Adriana Valdomar es estudiante en una escuela secundaria que se llama El corazón Sagrado. Tiene catorce años y es baja y delgada. Su cumpleaños es el veinte de octubre. Adriana tiene muchos amigos pero su mejor amiga es María. Adriana participa en deportes como voléibol y tenis, pero estudia todas las noches. Prefiere estudiar historia y literatura porque biología es muy difícil para ella.

Nombre: _____ Apellido: _____

Edad: _____ Fecha de nacimiento: _____

Físico: _____

Escuela: _____

Asignaturas favoritas: _____

Deportes: _____

C ¿Cuál es tu color favorito?

Do a survey of 20 people from your home, community or school, and find out what their favourite colour is. Present your information in the pie chart below, in Spanish.

1 Divide and colour the pie chart according to the number of persons who prefer each colour.

2 Label each colour.

3 State how many people prefer each colour next to its place on the pie chart.

Ejemplo: Rojo – 5 personas

D Tarea

Find out the required information about the following countries and fill in the chart.

País (Country)	Capital (Capital)	Moneda (Currency)	Colores de la bandera nacional (Colours of the national flag)
Jamaica			
Argentina			
Cuba			
Puerto Rico			
Trinidad y Tobago			
Panamá			

E Antónimos

Complete each sentence below with the opposite of the adjective used. Pay close attention to agreement with the person described.

1   Mi hermanita es gorda, pero mi hermano mayor es

_____ .

2   La clase de matemáticas es fácil pero la clase de literatura es

_____ .

3   Elena es una chica tímida, pero su amigo Reinaldo es muy

_____ .

4   Mi papá es trabajador pero mi tío Alfredo es muy

_____ .

5   La profesora es simpática, pero los estudiantes son

_____ .

F ¿Cómo es tu amiga?

Read the conversation below and then answer the questions that follow in English.

Javier: Hola Celi, ¿qué tal?

Araceli: Bien, Javier, y ¿cómo estás tú?

Andrew: Javier está super bien porque tiene una nueva amiguita.

Araceli: ¿Verdad, Javier? ¿Cómo es ella?

Javier: Primero, se llama Mariluz y es alta y delgada y bonita.

Andrew: No, Celi, Mariluz es alta pero es gordita.

Araceli: ¿Y su personalidad, Javier?

Andrew: Es habladora, generosa y muy paciente.

Javier: Por favor, Andrew, cállate. Mariluz es mi amiga. Ella es un poco introvertida pero muy interesante. Pero es verdad que es paciente y tolerante.

1   How is Javier feeling?

_____

2   What is the reason for his feelings?

_____

3   What is the name of the new person mentioned?

_____

4   How does Javier describe this person?

_____

5   What does Andrew say about her appearance?

_____

6   What does Andrew say about her personality?

_____

7   How does Javier react to what Andrew says?

_____

8   On what do Javier and Andrew agree?

_____

6 Querido diario

Here is what Ana wrote in her diary today to describe what she thinks about Javier.

12 de diciembre

Querido diario:

Hoy es un día muy hermoso e importante. ¡Javier y yo hablamos mucho! ¿Quién es Javier? Pues, es el amigo de mi hermano. Y Javier es un joven fuerte, atlético y muy guapo. Tiene el pelo rizado – su peinado es muy moderno. Tiene los ojos bonitos y siempre lleva un arete. Es serio y trabajador y pasa mucho tiempo en el gimnasio. ¡Tal vez por eso es tan fuerte!

Write a similar entry in a diary describing someone you know, either real or imaginary.

Fecha:

Querido Diario:

_____

_____

_____

_____

_____

_____

_____

_____

H En la tienda ¡Computadoras y más!

The six friends have received gift coupons for participating in the radio show. They leave the show and visit a store to use the coupons. Read the conversation and answer the questions in English.

Scene 1

Andrew: ¡Qué programa más estupendo!

Araceli: Sí, y los cupones de regalo son superbuenos, podemos comprar muchas cosas en esta tienda.

Scene 2

Mercedes: Esta computadora portátil es justamente lo que necesito. Es pequeña y fácil de usar.

Javier: Prefiero comprar estos audífonos de color azul y negro y estos videojuegos modernos e interesantes. Pero no sé si tengo bastante dinero.

Scene 3

Ana: Lo que realmente necesito es un radio despertador. Mercedes, mira los de color rojo y amarillo y de forma cuadrada.

Mercedes: ¡Qué aburrido! ¿Un radio despertador? ¿Por qué no compras otra cosa más interesante, Ana, como una grabadora?

Scene 4

Andrew: Este póster con la foto de Jennifer López es estupendo.

Michael: ¿Cuál? ¿El póster de color rojo, amarillo y blanco?

Araceli: No, Michael. Andrew habla del póster con Jennifer vestida de blanco y rojo. ¡Qué hermosa es!

---

1   Examine these new words and draw a line to match them with their meaning.

a los cupones de regalo   radio-alarm clock

b la computadora portátil   earphones

c los audífonos   video games

d los videojuegos   poster

e el radio despertador   gift tokens

f el póster   laptop computer

2   Using the information in the passage, complete each sentence below
    describing each item.

Ejemplo: Los cupones de regalo son superbuenos.

a   La computadora portátil es

_____

b   Los audífonos son

_____

c   Los videojuegos son

_____

d   El radio despertado es

_____

I Un amigo nuevo

Write an e-mail to a new friend and
respond to the questions he/she has
asked, below. Don't forget to say hello
and goodbye.

¿Cómo te llamas?

¿Cuántos años tienes?

¿Cuál es tu nacionalidad?

¿Cuál es tu color favorito?

¿Cuántas personas hay en tu familia?

¿Vives con tu familia?

¿Qué tal la relación con tu familia?

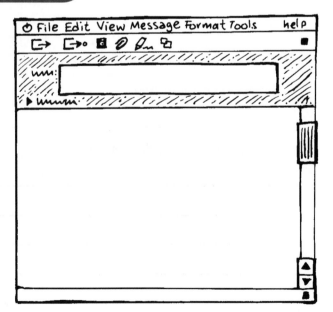

J Mi casa ideal

Draw or stick a picture of your ideal house here below. Write a short paragraph about it. Use adjectives to describe the rooms.

En mi casa ideal hay _____

_____

La cocina es grande y moderna. _____

_____

_____

_____

_____

7 Una gran pasión

A ¿Cómo es mi amigo?

Use the words given to describe your new Latin American friends.

Ejemplo: Javier y Andrew son independientes y confidentes.

1 Mercedes es _____ y _____. (reservado, sincero)

2 Michael y Andrew son _____ y _____. (aplicado, cómico)

3 Araceli es _____ y _____. (hablador, travieso)

4 Javier y Michael son _____ y _____. (fuerte, saludable)

5 Ana y Mercedes son _____ y _____. (inteligente, serio)

6 Ana y Michael son _____ y _____. (simpático, paciente)

7 Andrew es _____ y _____. (independiente, artístico)

8 Los cinco amigos son _____ y _____. (amistoso, responsable)

B Admiro a ...

Stick or draw pictures of people you admire here below, and say why you admire them.

Admiro a Perico porque es cómico e inteligente.

1

_____
_____

2

3

4

_____   _____   _____
_____   _____   _____

C Mi pasaporte

Pretend that you are an adult working in the profession of your dreams. Fill in the information about yourself below to apply for your new passport.

MINISTERIO DE SEGURIDAD NACIONAL

Nombre: _____ **Apellido:** _____

Edad: _____ **Sexo:** _____

Nacionalidad: _____

Profesión: _____

País de Nacimiento: _____

Dirección Actual:

(Calle) _____

(Ciudad) _____

(País) _____

Países visitados en los últimos cinco años:

País   **Duración de visita**

_____   _____

_____   _____

_____   _____

D ¿Cuál es su nacionalidad?

Complete the following.

Ejemplo: Esteban es de Puerto Rico. Su nacionalidad es puertorriqueño y vive en la capital San Juan.

1 Raúl es de Perú. Su nacionalidad es _____ y vive en la capital _____.

2 Silvia es de España.   Su nacionalidad es _____ y vive en la capital _____.

3 Albert es de Jamaica. Su nacionalidad es _____ y vive en la capital _____.

4 Cindy es de Barbados. Su nacionalidad es _____ y vive en la capital _____.

5 Bernardo es de Cuba. Su nacionalidad es _____ y vive en la capital _____.

6 Tomás es de Venezuela. Su nacionalidad es _____ y vive en la capital _____.

7 Blanca es de Panamá. Su nacionalidad es _____ y vive en la capital _____.

8 Adriana es de los Estados Unidos de América. Su nacionalidad es _____ y vive en la capital _____.

E La bandera nacional

Fill in the national flag of each country below and complete the sentences describing it.

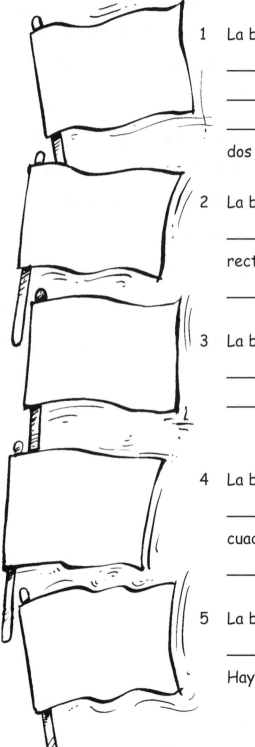

1 La bandera de Puerto Rico es

_____, _____ y

_____.Hay un triángulo

_____, tres rayas _____ y

dos rayas _____.

2 La bandera de México es _____,

_____ y _____. Hay un

rectángulo _____, un rectángulo

_____ y un rectángulo _____.

3 La bandera de España es _____, y

_____. Hay un rectángulo

_____ y dos rayas _____.

4 La bandera de Chile es _____,

_____ y _____. Hay un

cuadro _____, un rectángulo

_____ y un rectángulo _____.

5 La bandera de mi país es

_____.

Hay _____.

F La Copa Mundial

Fill in the blanks with the correct form of the adjective.

El fútbol es un deporte muy (común) _____ en el mundo. Hay

programas (excelente) _____ en la televisión con los partidos

(internacional) _____. Unos países son (famoso) _____

porque tienen futbolistas (talentoso) _____. Durante la Copa

Mundial, hay una gran pasión en el mundo y los colores de los equipos

(ganador) _____ son muy populares. En uno de los estadios

(moderno) _____ o en una casa (humilde) _____, los

espectadores son (cómodo) _____ mientras ven a sus equipos

(favorito) _____.

G ¿Qué carrera quieres seguir?

Conduct a survey of your classmates or a group of friends, in Spanish, to find out which profession they want to pursue. Use these questions:

¿Cuál es tu nombre?   **¿Qué carrera quieres seguir?**

Note down the answers given by boys and girls in the table below.

Nombre	Sexo	Profesión

Present your data on two pie charts. Do you find the results interesting?

You have interviewed a soccer player for your school magazine. You forgot to write down the questions you asked. Fill in the spaces below for the questions, to match the answers you were given.

1

Soy Mario Torres.

2

Soy de Ecuador, pero vivo en Venezuela.

3

Precisamente, vivo ahora en Caracas.

4

Soy futbolista para un club venezolano. Hay un partido mañana en tu país.

5

Tengo 33 años, soy joven, ¿no?

6

Mi cumpleaños es el 10 de abril.

7

Hay cuatrol; en mi familia dos hermanos, mi madre y yo. Mi familia vive en Ecuador.

8

Muchas gracias. Y chao.

I Nuestro Caribe

Your teacher will now play track 30 on the CD, titled 'Nuestro Caribe'. Before you listen, read the passage below to get a general sense of what you will hear.

El Caribe es una región muy _____ en el mundo. En los _____

del Caribe, hay gente que habla idiomas _____ incluso inglés y

_____. También hay una gran variedad de comidas, _____

y razas. Muchos _____ visitan el Caribe cada _____. Los

caribeños son muy _____ de nuestra región y nuestra cultura.

Somos como una _____ grande aquí en _____ Caribe.

1   Say in one sentence what you think the passage is about.

   _____

2   Match the word and meanings.

región	variety
mundo	people
gente	culture
idiomas	races
incluso	world
variedad	visit
razas	region
visitan	languages
cultura	including

3   Guess what some of the missing words might be and list them.

_____

_____

_____

4   Now listen to the passage and fill in the missing words.

J Otros vencedores

Listen carefully to track 31 on the CD. Circle the corresponding letter of the correct answer.

1   Hay _____ ganadores
    a 4
    b 14
    c 40

2   La competencia se llama _____
    a La Copa de América Latina
    b La Copa Mundial
    c La Copa Caribeña

3   El señor Ayala es _____
    a paraguayo
    b guatemalteco
    c colombiano

4   El señor Ayala tiene _____ años.
    a 39
    b 29
    c 19

5 El señor Ayala es _____

   a cocinero

   b técnica

   c oficinista

6 La señorita Carmen Jiménez es de _____

   a Paraguay

   b Perú

   c Colombia

7 La señorita Carmen Jiménez tiene entre _____

   a 15 y 20 años

   b 21 y 25 años

   c 26 y 30

8 Juan Pablo Morales es _____

   a estadounidense

   b puertorriqueño

   c peruano

9 Jorge Reinaldo tiene _____

   a más de 53 años

   b menos de 53 años

   c 53 años

10 Jorge Reinaldo habla _____

   a español

   b inglés

   c francés

8 ¡Qué desilusión!

A Suena el timbre...

Draw in six of the times that your school bell rings, on the clocks below.
Write the time in Spanish underneath.

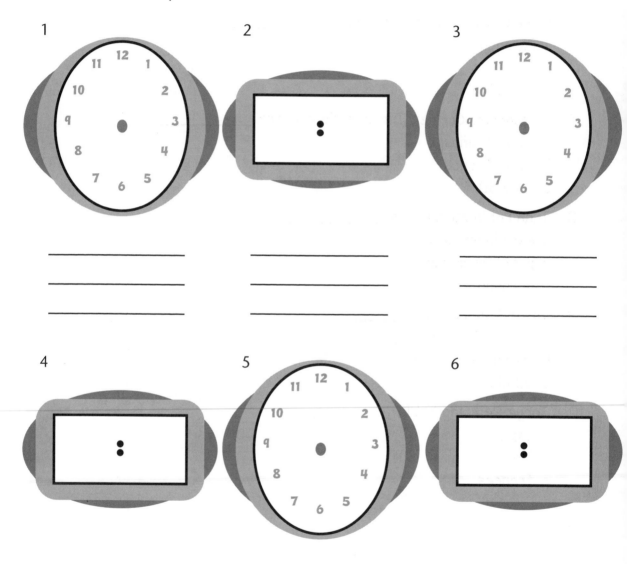

1

2

3

_____
_____
_____

4

5

6

_____
_____
_____

B Hoy, en la emisora de radio...

Here is a part of a schedule for a radio station. What time does the announcer say at the start of each programme? Write the time in Spanish in words.

3.30	Partido de fútbol: Club Juventud vs. Club Oriental
5.00	Noticias internacionales – BBC
5.15	Reportaje de tráfico
5.25	Pronóstico nacional
5.40	Música con Jaime
7.00	Noticias nacionales
7.10	A discutir – la política y usted
9.05	Música para el oyente

1 _____

2 _____

3 _____

4 _____

5 _____

6 _____

7 _____

8 _____

C ¿Qué hora es, Ana?

Your teacher is now going to play track 33 on the CD. Listen to Ana telling Mercedes the time and fill in the time she says below.

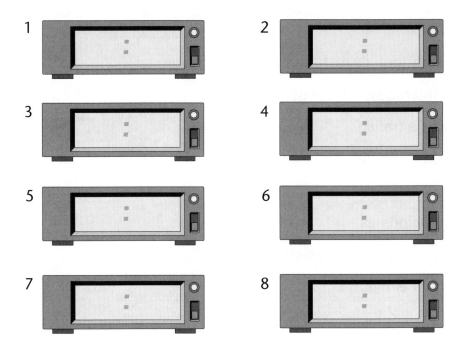

D ¿Comprendes las palabras?

Sort the following words into the correct columns.

media   llano   fresco   invierno   montaña   medianoche   viento   seca
nublado   desierto   playa   minuto   cuarto   verano   frío   selva

Hora	Estación	Tiempo	Paisaje

E ¿Qué tiempo hace?

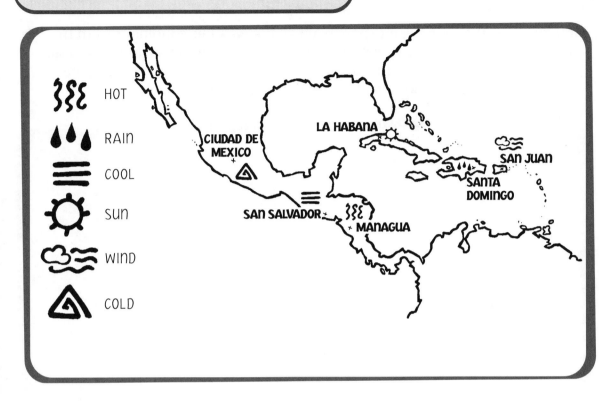

𝄞	HOT
💧	RAIN
≡	COOL
☀	SUN
☁	WIND
△	COLD

Write a sentence to say what the weather is like in each of the capital cities shown on the map.

1   En San Salvador

_____.

2   En Managua

_____.

3   En Santo Domingo

_____.

4   En La Habana

_____.

5   En San Juan

_____.

6   En la Ciudad de México

_____.

F En mi pueblo, hace ...

Imagine that the Caribbean experienced all the weather conditions from the previous exercise. Sketch a map of your country and put in six towns and six different weather symbols. In class, take turns to ask and answer questions with a partner describing what the weather is like in each town.

G El tiempo en el Caribe ...

You are on a student chat room on the Internet. Answer these questions.

1   ¿Hay invierno en el Caribe?

_____

2   ¿Qué tiempo hace en diciembre en tu país?

_____

3   ¿Qué estaciones hay en el Caribe?

_____

4   ¿Hay desiertos en tu país?

_____

5   ¿Qué más hay en tu país?

_____

H ¿Dónde está ...?

Identify in which countries these famous natural features are found.

1   La selva Amazon está en

_____.

2   El río Amazonas está en

_____.

3   Las montañas Andes están en

_____.

4   La playa Acapulco está en

_____.

5   El desierto Atacama está en

_____.

I Me presento...

You have just joined an Internet club for students of Spanish. Write a brief introduction of yourself in Spanish. Include the following:

1 Your name and nationality.
2 Your age and birthday.
3 A description of yourself.
4 What profession you want to follow.
5 Something about your friends.
6 Something about your country.
7 How you feel about your country.

9 La cita

A Playa Bella

Look at the brochure on the following page. Answer the following questions.

1   What kind of vacation is offered?

_____

2   How long is it?

_____

3   What is included?

_____

4   What facilities are there?

_____

_____

5   List the places that can be visited.

_____

6   List two adjectives that demonstrate what kind of facility it is.

_____

Playa Bella

Vacaciones ideales con sol y mar

Una semana

Hotel, comida y transporte incluidos

Facilidades modernas:
- hotel lujoso 5 estrellas
- 3 restaurantes
- 5 piscinas
- discoteca
- gimnasio
- spa

Visitas a:
- Centro Comercial Tropibana
- Plaza famosa San Martín
- Iglesia histórica de María Santísima

B En la habitación de Araceli

Araceli is supposed to tidy up her room. Her mother keeps calling out questions. Say where everything really is.

Ejemplo: **Mamá:** Araceli, ¿las revistas están en la mesa?

   Araceli: Sí, mamá.

Las revistas <u>están en</u> la mesa.

1 **Mamá:** Araceli, ¿la mesa está a la ventana?

   Araceli: No, mamá.

   La mesa _____ armario
   y la puerta.

2 **Mamá:** Araceli, ¿el teléfono está sobre la mesa?

   Araceli: No, mamá.

   El teléfono _____ silla.

3 **Mamá:** Araceli, ¿la silla está cerca del escritorio?

   Araceli: No, mamá.

   La silla _____ escritorio.

4 **Mamá:** Araceli, ¿los zapatos están en el armario?

   Araceli: No, mamá.

   Los zapatos _____ escritorio.

5 **Mamá:** Araceli, ¿la mochila está debajo del escritorio?

   Araceli: No, mamá.

   La mochila _____ puerta.

6 **Mamá:** Araceli, ¿las novelas están sobre el estante?

   Araceli: No, mamá.

   Las novelas _____ cama.

7 **Mamá:** Araceli, ¿la lámpara está sobre la mesa?

   Araceli: No, mamá.

   La lámpara _____ mesa.

C Situaciones

What would you say in each of the following situations in Spanish?

1   Say what your best friend is like.

_____.

2   Tell someone the colours of your national flag.

_____.

3   A foreigner asks if there is winter in your country. What do you reply?

_____.

4   Someone asks you the time just as the first school bell of the day rings. What do you reply?

_____.

5   Ask your friend where his/her mother works.

_____.

6   It is your birthday and someone asks how you feel. What do you say?

_____.

7   Tell a penfriend that you are from the Caribbean.

_____.

8   Suggest to your friends that you all go to the cinema.

_____.

D ¿Aquí hay tiendas?

Your friend is shopping in Panama, but keeps going to the wrong places to buy items. Tell him to go to the correct locations.

1   Perdone, ¿aquí hay helados?

Aquí no, hay helados en _____.

2   Perdone, ¿aquí hay discos compactos?

Aquí no, hay discos compactos en _____.   63

3   Perdone, ¿aquí hay libros?

Aquí no, hay libros en _____.

4   Perdone, ¿aquí hay frutas?

Aquí no, hay frutas en _____.

5   Perdone, ¿aquí hay juguetes?

Aquí no, hay juguetes en _____.

6   Perdone, ¿aquí hay pan?

Aquí no, hay pan en _____.

7   Perdone, ¿aquí hay zapatos?

Aquí no, hay zapatos en _____.

8   Perdone, ¿aquí hay joyas?

Aquí no, hay joyas en _____.

E Alfonso y Enrique

Read the following passage and fill in the spaces with the correct verb.

Me (1)_____ Alfonso y (2)_____

colombiano. Hoy (3)_____ viernes y (4)_____ en

mi clase a la escuela. (5)_____ mucho calor y

(6)_____ fatigado. Mi amigo Enrique (7)_____

muy animado. Normalmente Enrique ___(8)_____ perezoso pero

mañana (9)_____ sábado y por eso (10)_____

muy contento y animado.

64

F ¿Adónde vamos?

You and your friends would like to go out. Write a sentence which suggests you all go to each venue below.

Ejemplo: Ice-cream parlour.
¿Por qué no vamos a la heladería?

1 _____
_____.

2 _____
_____.

3 _____
_____.

4 _____
_____.

5 _____
_____.

6 _____
_____.

G Trabaja en...

Listen to track 38 on the CD and fill in the blanks saying who works at these places. Choose from the list below. Check the meanings of words you do not know.

médico   dependiente   taxista   agricultor   camarero   profesor
vendedor   reportero

1 _____

trabaja en la escuela.

2 _____

trabaja en el campo.

3 _____

trabaja en el mercado.

4 _____

trabaja en el restaurante.

5 _____

trabaja en el hospital.

6 _____

trabaja en la calle.

7 _____

trabaja en la oficina.

8 _____

trabaja en la tienda.

H Estoy ocupada

Esteban is trying to organize a date with his friend Natalia. Look at the
Natalia's diary and fill in the missing words in the dialogue.

Domingo:	a.m.	iglesia con mamá.
	p.m.	visita a los abuelos
Lunes:	a.m.	trabajo
	p.m.	conferencia con el director
Martes:	a.m.	trabajo
	p.m.	gimnasio

Miércoles:	a.m.	trabajo
	p.m.	cine con Tomás
Jueves:	a.m.	trabajo
	p.m.	libre
Viernes:	a.m.	trabajo
	p.m.	centro comercial con mi hermana
Sábado:	a.m.	visita al dentista
	p.m.	libre

Esteban: Aló, Natalia. ¿Cómo estás?

Natalia: (1) _____ bien, gracias. ¿Y tú?

Esteban: Estoy bien, pero aburrido. ¿Quieres ir al (2) _____ conmigo?
Hay una película muy buena.

Natalia: Lo siento, no puedo. Estoy (3) _____ hoy. Esta mañana

voy a la iglesia y por la (4) _____ visito a mis abuelos.

Esteban: Y mañana por la tarde, ¿(5) _____ libre?

Natalia: No, tengo una conferencia con mi director.

Esteban: ¿Cuándo estás (6) _____?

Natalia: El (7) _____ por la tarde, no tengo cita.

Esteban: Ay, esta tarde yo trabajo.

Natalia: También estoy libre el (8) _____ (9) _____ la tarde.

Esteban: Qué suerte. Yo también. Pues, ¿vamos al cine el sábado por la
tarde?

Natalia: Como no. Hasta el (10) _____. Gracias Esteban, y chao.

I Mi amigo es como...

Here is a sentence comparing someone to something. Match the words given and make your own sentences, by following the example.

Ejemplo: Mi amigo es fuerte como una roca.

lindo   el viento

brillante   una flor

frío   la nieve

callado   la noche

libre   el sol

1 _____

2 _____

3 _____

4 _____

5 _____

10 ¡Vamos, pues!

A Sopa de letras – la ropa

Find at least 20 Spanish words relating to the title above. Write the Spanish and English equivalent for each word that you find.

```
E  N  C  A  J  E  I  Z  J  A  B  U  S  X
C  I  A  X  U  N  P  A  P  L  R  U  O  I
A  Z  L  L  N  I  L  P  A  J  A  H  M  C
M  D  C  A  I  L  Z  A  O  T  G  U  B  O
I  A  E  T  F  N  U  T  R  E  A  X  R  R
S  C  T  S  O  L  O  O  E  S  S  T  E  B
E  I  I  E  R  R  A  S  U  E  T  E  R  A
T  N  N  V  M  X  O  L  C  D  O  N  O  T
A  U  E  S  E  U  B  L  A  N  V  O  S  A
L  T  S  T  S  N  X  G  Z  A  E  D  A  S
A  D  L  A  F  O  C  B  O  T  I  O  L  Z
N  Z  T  R  A  J  E  D  E  R  D  G  E  V
A  O  D  I  T  S  E  V  M  U  R  L  O  U
B  V  U  N  Z  S  A  T  E  U  Q  A  H  C
```

1 _____	11 _____
2 _____	12 _____
3 _____	13 _____
4 _____	14 _____
5 _____	15 _____
6 _____	16 _____
7 _____	17 _____
8 _____	18 _____
9 _____	19 _____
10 _____	20 _____

Write suitable responses in Spanish for the following situations.

1 You want to know where your friend is going. What do you ask him/her?

_____

2 What does he/she reply?

_____

3 You need to use the rest room. How do you ask your teacher's permission?

_____

4 Your mother would like more information about a class trip. How do you inform her when and where you and the class are going?

_____

5 You are in a store trying to decide whether a pair of pants goes well with a blouse you have chosen. What opinion does the shop attendant give?

_____

6 How do you ask the shop attendant what material the blue pants are made of?

_____

7 What does the shop attendant say?

_____

8 Some of your classmates are on their way to the office. Tell another friend where they are going.

_____

9 Tell a classmate that you want to go to her birthday party.

_____

10 What response would you write to the question ¿**Cuántos días hay en el año?**

_____

C ¿Quién va?

Your teacher will now play track 41 on the CD. For each question, you will hear a statement. Each statement is read only once, so you must listen very carefully. Look at the series of pictures for each question and select the one which best illustrates the statement you hear.

For example, you hear: **Los jóvenes van a la playa.**
Now look at the pictures.

The correct answer is C so you would circle the corresponding letter in your book.

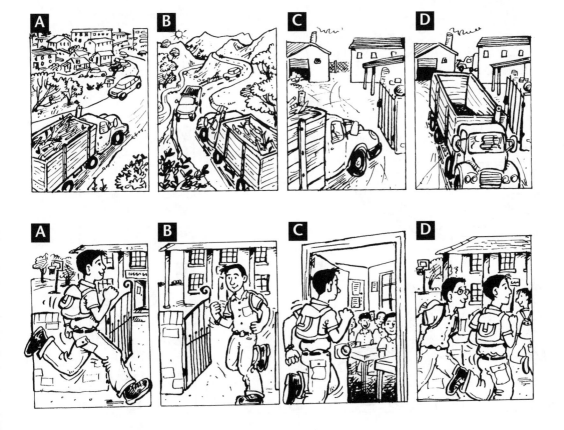

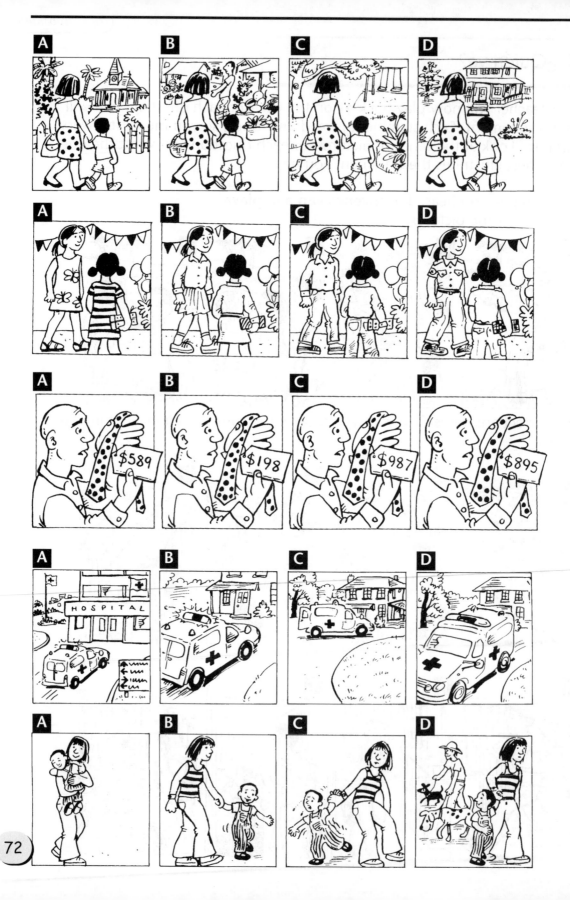

D ¿Voy, vas, va, vamos o van?

Complete each sentence with the correct part of the verb **ir**.

1 Yo siempre _____ a la escuela a las siete y media de la mañana.

2 Ellas _____ a la iglesia cada domingo.

3 Pedro nunca _____ al museo.

4 Nosotros _____ al cine los sábados por la noche.

5 Usted _____ a la playa los fines de semana.

6 Tú _____ al restaurante con tus padres.

7 Anita siempre _____ a la tienda los miércoles por la tarde.

8 Mi amigo y yo _____ al centro comercial cada tarde.

9 Yo no _____ al teatro.

10 Las mujeres _____ al supermercado después del trabajo.

11 ¡Hola, Pedro! ¿Cómo te _____?

12 Las botas negros _____ bien con la chaqueta de cuero.

13 Ya son las tres. ¡_____, pues!

14 ¿Adónde _____ María y su hermana?

15 Andrea, ya _____ a la fiesta, no?

E ¿Qué, quién, dónde?

Fill in the blanks to complete the table with the appropriate items, people and places.

¿Qué?	¿Quién?	¿Dónde?
Carne	carnicero	1 _____
2 _____	3 _____	zapatería
libros	4 _____	5 _____
6 _____	joyero	7 _____
helado	8 _____	heladería
pescado	9 _____	10 _____

F La tienda de Lucía

Read the flyer below and answer the questions that follow in English.

Tienda de Lucía

PRECIOS BAJOS

VENTA

Sólo este sábado y domingo, 14 y 15 de marzo
Entre las 6 de la mañana y as 6 de la tarde

Descuento de 50%

✓ Camisas de algodón

✓ Bufandas de encaje

✓ Corbatas de seda

✓ Relojes de oro

✓ Cinturones de cuero

Descuento de 20%

✓ Medias de nilón

✓ Faldas de lino

✓ Blusas de algodón

✓ Zapatos de cuero

✓ Bolsas y monederos de cuero

Premio especial para el primer cliente

Dirección: Calle Madrigal, número 175

Teléfono: 787 – 434 - 1380

En línea: www.tiendadelucia.com

1   What is the name of the store?

_____

2   When is the sale?

_____

3   What hours will the store be open?

_____

4   To whom is a special prize offered?

_____

5   Name two items that have a 50% discount.

_____

6   Name two items that have a 20% discount.

_____

7   What other information is given about the store?

_____

11 ¡Así me gusta!

A Cabeza, cintura, rodillas y pies...

1 Unscramble the following words which are all parts of the body.

a beaazc _____

b leop _____

c neetrf _____

d sooj _____

e rinza _____

f jearo _____

g loeucl _____

h hoosrbm _____

i chepo _____

j zbroa _____

k dooc _____

l moan _____

m sddeo _____

n ieanpr _____

o rildalo _____

p epis _____

2 Use the vocabulary above to label the illustration below.
  Draw lines to connect each part with the Spanish equivalent.

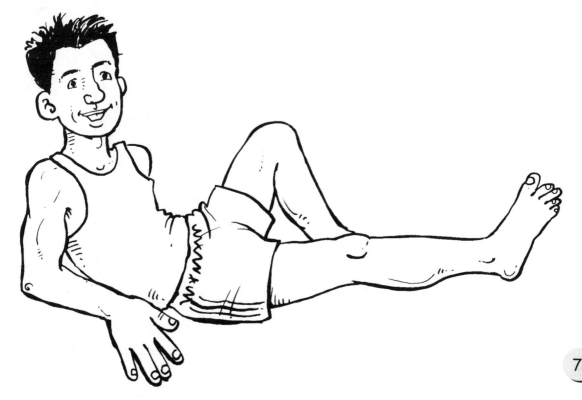

B ¿Cómo se sienten?

Look at each of the following illustrations and complete each sentence with an appropriate **tener** idiom.

1   El hombre _____

_____

2   Los niños _____

_____

3   El señor desafortunado no

_____

_____

4   Andrés _____

_____

5   Hoy, Juan _____

_____

6   Esta noche, Conchita

_____

_____

7   La profesora está
    enfadada porque Pedro siempre

_____

en su clase.

8   Nosotros siempre _____

_____

cuando van a cruzar la calle.

9   La familia Gómez _____

_____

cada mañana.

10 Yo soy muy popular y

_____

_____

Write suitable responses in Spanish to each of the following situations.

1 You and your classmates are having lunch in the cafeteria. Your friend would like to know what plans you have for the weekend. What does she ask?

_____

2 What do you reply to her question?

_____

3 Someone would like you to try a food item that you dislike. What do you say?

_____

4 One friend would like to know some of the foods you like to eat. What question does he ask?

_____

5 How do you respond?

_____

6 Your best friend prefers one item to another. What does she comment?

_____

7 You have finished your cold drink and still feel thirsty. What do you say?

_____

8 Your friend thinks you are thirsty because it is so hot. What does he say?

_____

9 You leave the table to purchase another cold drink. How do you inform your classmates of your intention?

_____

10 Your friend would like you to buy a snack for him, as he feels hungry. What favour does he ask after stating how he feels?

_____

D ¿Qué vas a comer?

Write four appropriate items for each meal. Include one drink. You may need your dictionary for additional items.

El desayuno (Breakfast)

1 _____   2 _____

3 _____   4 _____

El almuerzo (Lunch)

5 _____   6 _____

7 _____   8 _____

La cena (Dinner)

9 _____   10 _____

11 _____   12 _____

Search for the Spanish equivalent of verbs listed below the puzzle.

R	A	J	A	L	E	R	R	A	R	T	N	E	L
A	D	I	V	I	N	A	R	R	E	A	R	I	U
R	A	G	E	L	L	H	U	C	A	R	M	R	C
R	A	V	A	L	R	C	U	H	I	P	R	A	H
A	R	G	E	E	N	U	G	B	I	E	M	L	A
R	E	E	R	V	A	C	U	A	B	I	I	A	R
R	R	R	I	A	D	S	R	E	N	A	R	R	C
O	A	V	P	R	A	E	B	A	A	A	A	I	O
B	A	I	L	A	R	A	R	V	R	L	R	R	M
A	Ñ	A	R	A	I	D	U	T	S	E	B	B	E
T	A	R	T	R	E	R	E	N	S	E	Ñ	A	R
R	R	N	R	A	R	B	E	L	E	C	A	R	H
O	A	P	R	E	N	D	E	R	R	I	V	I	V
C	O	M	P	R	A	R	I	B	I	R	C	S	E

to sweep	to swim	to walk
to write	to dance	to love
to read	to study	to look
to eat	to erase	to listen to
to drink	to wash	to celebrate
to live	to enter	to wear, carry
to learn	to clean	to arrive
to climb	to win	to teach
to open	to buy	to relax
to sing	to fight	to guess

12 ¡Qué diversión!

A Un día típico en la vida de Juan Carlos

Look at the series of pictures that illustrate how Juan Carlos spends his typical day. Write a sentence in Spanish below each picture describing his actions. Mention the time and place where appropriate. Number 1 has been done to give you an example.

1

El reloj de Carlos alarma a las cinco de la mañana

2

3

4

5

6 _____

_____

_____

7 _____

_____

_____

8 _____

_____

_____

9 _____

_____

_____

10 _____

_____

_____

11 _____

_____

_____

B ¿Cómo ganas la vida?

A journalist asks each professional how he/she earns a living. Write their response in Spanish in the space provided. Number 1 has been done to give you an example.

1   Periodista: Señorita, ¿cómo ganas la vida?
                       Una criada: Yo limpio la casa.

2   Periodista: Señor, ¿cómo ganas la vida?

    Un pintor: _____

3   Periodista: Señorita, ¿cómo ganas la vida?

    Una cantante: _____

4   Periodista: Señor, ¿cómo ganas la vida?

    Un autor: _____

5   Periodista: Y usted, señora, ¿cómo ganas la vida?

    Una profesora: _____

6   Periodista: Señor, ¿cómo ganas la vida?

    Un fotógrafo: _____

7   Periodista: Señor, ¿cómo ganas la vida?

    Un mecánico: _____

8   Periodista: Señor, ¿cómo ganas la vida?

    Un cartero: _____

9   Periodista: Señor, ¿cómo ganas la vida?

    Un conductor*:   _____

10 Periodista: Señora, ¿cómo ganas la vida?

    Una vendedora: _____

* Driver

C ¿Qué hacen?

1 Write an appropriate Spanish verb that describes what each of the following parts of the body does. Remember the verb must agree with the subject.

a   Los ojos _____ .

b   Las orejas _____ .

c   La boca _____ y _____ .

d   Las manos _____ , _____ y

_____ .

e   Los pies _____ , _____ , y

_____ .

2 Complete the sentences to describe what these persons do at the places mentioned.

a   Ana y Andrew _____ las películas al cine.

b   Araceli y Mercedes _____ mucha ropa en el centro comercial.

c   Javier y Michael _____ una comida especial en el restaurante.

d   Los amigos _____ y _____ en la escuela todos los días.

e   Los señores Ramdial _____ en el jardín por las tardes.

f   Araceli y sus amigas _____ y

_____ en el club para jóvenes.

g   Los profesores siempre _____ y

_____ en la clase.

D El horario de campamento

Listen carefully as your teacher plays track 44 on the CD. Andrew talks about what he does at camp. Answer the following questions in English.

1 When does Andrew go to camp?

_____

2 What does Andrew do on Monday and Wednesday mornings?

_____

3 When does Andrew go to Art class?

_____

4 What does Andrew learn in Art class?

_____

5 What does Andrew do on Tuesdays?

_____

6 When does Andrew have kitchen duty?

_____

7 What does Andrew do when he is on kitchen duty?

_____

8 What is 'El círculo'?

_____

9 Name two other activities in which Andrew participates over the weekend.

_____

10 How does Andrew feel about summer camp? Why?

_____

_____

Unscramble the Spanish words below. Write the letters in the space provided.
Clue: They are all words you have learnt in units 11 and 12.

O E C R M

S I T D A E R U

E R E L

A A C n T R

V R L A A

I A n P R T

A T R C O

E E B R B

R C R O E R

LO QUE EXCLAMA
EL ESTUDIANTE
CUANDO TERMINA
LA CLASE DE
ESPAÑOL

¡AHORA

LOS ！

Now arrange the circled letters to form the answer to the question below the
illustration. Write your answer in the spaces provided below.

Respuesta: _____